treehouse genies

This edition produced by Treehouse Genies Ltd
34 The Ridgeway, London, N11 3LJ

1 3 5 7 9 10 8 6 4 2

Author: Sara Jackson
Design: Karen Shooter
Strategy & Drive: Melanie Cohen
Illustration: Anton Brand & Jim Hanson
Additional Creative: Jessica Cohen

Printed in England.

ISBN: 978-1-9993004-1-8

With the support and help of

THE CECIL ROSEN FOUNDATION

camp **simcha**
supporting families with serious childhood illness

Discover more at
treehousegenies.com

The Treehouse at Number 9

Heroes Day

SARA JACKSON   **KAREN SHOOTER**   **MEL COHEN**   with Jess Cohen

Meet the family...

Here's a little reminder of the family who live at Number 9.

JeaN GeNie

Mummy Carey

TEd

Baxter

The Genies Gang...

And of course, here are the Genies... each one as friendly as the next.

Lugs

aNgEl

Flo

Cee-Cee

Freddie

Macro

Oscar

Arty

Pip

It's 4:15, the doorbell rings and Genies barrel through.
They take off coats and hats and bags and now and then a shoe,
Then run out to the garden and the Treehouse that awaits
Where they love to spend their after-school with all their funny mates.

Meanwhile in the Treehouse they all play and laugh and chat,
As Bax the dog runs up and down while barking at the cat.
When Joe comes in he notices that Cee-Cee looks quite low
Though she's trying not to show it, which begins to worry Joe.

From outside Teddy yells "Grub's up. Will someone let me in?"
As he stands there with the treats that Granny made and gave to him.
Flo comes bounding down the stairs and takes the load from Ted,
As she knows her friends won't settle 'til they're well and truly fed.

They hand out cakes and giggle at the toppings Granny made
There are bees and ants and snails in there, a lovely bug parade.
Pip is smiling extra wide at something Freddie's drawn,
Arty strums a tune and Angel stifles a big yawn.

Lugs wolfs down a spider cake and smiling licks his lips,
Then he dashes to the cupboard where he hopes to find some tips
From the Duke who tries to leave some clever tidbits there each day;
Lugs isn't disappointed, so Freddie yells "Hooray!".

Duke has made an insect quiz that Angel now reads out
Everybody gathers close to hear what it's about.
Macro hears a scratching sound, so crouches down to look
Where he finds our Bax's bone, behind the chair under a book.

Oscar's in a happy mood and telling all the team
About his funny day at school and how his lunchtime made him beam.
The fun began with Pip who simply loves to put on shows,
But today she laughed too hard and snorted milk out of her nose.

Cee-Cee's trying very hard to smile and join right in,
But when Joe says she's not quite right her tears at last begin.
Today was hard because some girls were mean and so unfair,
"They ridiculed my glasses and my stupid bright red hair".

The kids all gather round and try to wipe her tears away
While Arty strums a tune and Freddie also starts to play.
Flo says "red's a colour that is strong and full of fire"
So celebrate your super power and use it to inspire!"

Pip grabs a pen and starts to draw a picture on the wall
In bright red hue "It's Super Ceec!" emerges from her scrawl.
They all take pens and glitter and they join in with this game
As Cee-Cee finds her smile and draws her own big burning flame.

When home-time comes they start to leave while clutching in their hands A "SuperFriend" memento on a fiery red wristband.

Joe whispers to them all a little
something as they go,
It's to do with Heroes Day but
what he says we don't yet know.

Next morning Joe rings on for Cee-Cee as he does each day
And he's happy to discover that she's chased her blues away.
Carey takes her arm, resplendent in a bright red hat
And they both walk on together catching up on this and that.

Joe, Ted and Duke run on ahead to see who'll win today
While Carey talks to Cee-Cee to make sure she's quite ok.
"Joe told me that those girls were mean, it's not fair what they said
But now you see how strong you are, be proud of your red.

Cee-Cee holds her head up high and marches into school
Where she gasps in shock at what she sees, it really is quite cool,
"You're dressed as me" she splutters to her friends who all agree
"I can't believe from all those options that you've chosen me?!"

A LITTLE BIT MORE ABOUT OUR GENIES...

Find out what makes the Genies Gang so special...

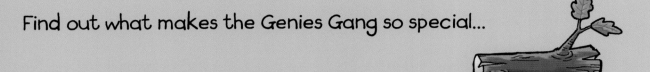

FLO has **Sickle Cell Anaemia**. This means her blood cells are not round, but look like a sickle or banana instead. This causes her pain and other medical problems and she sometimes needs blood transfusions to help.

....

ANGEL has **Brittle Bone Disorder**. Her bones break very easily, even by walking up the stairs or just sitting down. Aside from the pain, this causes problems with growth and it is important that she takes extra special care.

....

OSCAR has **Cockayne Syndrome** which means his body ages much faster than yours or mine. This means that his eyesight, hearing, heart and body will weaken as he grows.

....

MACRO has **Achondroplasia**, which means he has short stature. His limbs don't grow at the same rate as the rest of his body and there are some medical problems connected to this.

....

CEE-CEE is **partially sighted** which means she can see but not as well as other people. This makes all kinds of things a challenge for her as she goes about her day.

ARTY has **allergies** so needs his medicine with him all the time. He takes extra care to avoid touching or eating things that could make him very unwell, and makes sure others understand and help him to avoid them.

. . . .

LUGS is hard of hearing due to **Otosclerosis**, a condition of the middle ear. So it is difficult for him in conversations, on busy streets or in a loud classroom. His hearing will probably get worse as he grows older.

. . . .

TED has something called **HED** which he inherited from his Mummy. He has very little hair, not many teeth and his body isn't able to sweat. This makes life a bit complicated but his family know how to help him.

. . . .

PIP has a condition called **NF2**. This causes the nerve cells in her body to get a bit confused, making them stick together instead of moving around. This means she can often be in pain and has to have regular check-ups with her doctors.

. . . .

FREDDIE has **Down's Syndrome** which means that he has an extra Chromosome 21. He needs extra support at school and home with learning and some other skills, and he has to have regular check ups with his doctors to be sure that he is growing up as healthy as can be.

. . . .

JOE, while unaffected, is a special kind of big brother, which is why he has so many friends. He has always helped his mum and little brother and is kind, tolerant and full of imagination and fun.

The Treehouse Team

The Treehouse At Number Nine is a resource for charities and families who live within the world of difference.

When Sara Jackson's eldest was entering his terrible 2's, his baby brother had just been diagnosed with a rare genetic condition. Desperate for books to help the family during this difficult time, she found nothing suitable or uplifting in the market. With a career in TV drama and a passion for storytelling, she decided to write her own and turned to her friend, fellow creative mum and established graphic designer Karen Shooter, to join forces. With Karen's background in Children's publishing and design and Sara's words, together over the following years they collaborated while balancing life as working mothers, and what emerged were some beautifully designed children's stories.

When Mel Cohen's daughter Jess was 11 she suddenly became very ill and was subsequently diagnosed with a rare genetic condition. On the outside she continued to look like the Jess everyone knew and loved, but was struggling to come to terms with her complex diagnosis. Mel, with her background in strategic marketing and research, recognised how difficult it was for both Jess and the family to communicate and was desperately seeking a positive way to approach the diagnosis and their new futures.

As old friends of Sara and Karen, Mel reached out to the pair, having discovered that The Treehouse at No.9's Musical Story App had become a positive force for Jess and their family. Jess subsequently became The Treehouse at No.9's Young Ambassador and found her voice. Across their journey together Jess has designed two new characters for the Genies Gang and has visited schools and charities to help introduce them. Mel has since come on board officially to form the third branch of the Treehouse at No. 9 and together they make a well-balanced and powerful team.

Sara   Karen   Mel   Jess